Nicky
Knitting Granny
and the Cat

Nicky's Granny used to knit
Enormous jerseys that would fit
An elephant or a giraffe.
She knitted till the cat would laugh

At scarves that never seemed
                    to stop
And caps with bobbles
                    on the top,

And mufflers long as
                   any street
That tangled all round
                   Nicky's feet.

She wrapped the bird cage in the hall

And tucked the parrot in a shawl

She said the goldfish should not swim
With only scales to cover him.

She made a swimsuit that would do
To keep him warm the winter through,

And also knitted (dear kind soul!)
A cosy for the goldfish bowl.

She clothed the fern and knitted lots

of comforters for cactus pots,

Curtains, a carpet for the stairs,

And woollies for
the banisters —

Until, with lots of wool to knit,
There seemed no more to do with it.
Gran looked around her in despair
And thrust the needles through her hair,

Just then the cat in reckless play
Patted a ball of wool away.
Whereat she gave a joyful yell:
'*He* needs a cardigan as well!'

She made it soon and boldly tried
to fit the squirming cat inside

Though Nicky cried that lack of breath
Would cause the creature's instant death.

But not a bit! With frenzied swirl

Unravelling yards of plain and purl,

It sprang into the window-seat.
(The things it said I won't repeat.)

Gran tried to soothe it, all in vain.
The cat rushed up the stairs again

And clawed the carpet out, and tore

The curtains down
upon the floor,

It broke the goldfish bowl in rage,
And stunned Gran with the parrot's cage,

Creating chaos far and wide,
Then sat and laughed until it cried.